CIRIA C649

London, 2006

Books are to be returned on or before
the last date below.

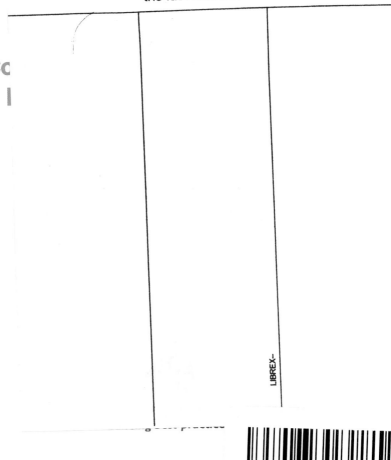

Cc

l

LIBREX–

D1612567

Classic House, 174–180 Old Street, L
Telephone +44 (0)20 754S
Fax +44 (0)20 7253 0523
Email enquiries@ciria.org
Website www.ciria.org

Control of water pollution from linear construction projects. Site guide.

Murnane, E; Heap, A; Swain, A

CIRIA

CIRIA C649   © 2006 CIRIA   RP708   ISBN-13: 978-0-86017-649-1
ISBN-10: 0-86017-649-5

British Library Cataloguing in Publication Data

A catalogue record is available for this book from the British Library.

Keywords
Construction management, environmental good practice, pollution prevention, rivers and waterways, site management, water quality

Reader interest	Classification	
Pollution prevention, linear construction, surface water, groundwater, construction cycle, pollution migration	AVAILABILITY	Unrestricted
	CONTENT	Advice/guidance
	STATUS	Committee-guided
	USER	Construction professionals, managers and site staff

Published by CIRIA, Classic House, 174–180 Old Street, London EC1V 9BP, UK.

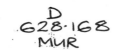

Efforts are being made at all levels within the construction industry to improve environmental performance. Everyone involved in the construction and maintenance of infrastructure developments needs to be aware of their environmental obligations and the benefits that best practice will bring to a construction project. You are responsible for ensuring your work and the work of those you manage does not pollute the water environment. Using the good practice advice in this guide you will be able to identify appropriate methods of protecting the water environment while carrying out your activities on site.

This guide is relevant to all construction personnel, and particularly to those working on linear projects (highways, railways, pipelines, cables and inland waterways), which have the following challenges:

- site activities move along a "corridor"
- routes cross varied ground conditions, soil types and water environments
- sites have numerous access points, site compounds and haul routes
- land take may be restricted
- routes can have a variety of neighbours and regulatory controls.

The guide has been written specifically for on-site use by:

- site engineers and construction managers
- site foremen and site supervisors.

To accompany this guide, CIRIA has also produced technical guidance (publication C648), which is aimed at clients, designers, regulators, environmental consultants, construction managers and site environmental managers in both the design and construction phases of a project.

This guide provides good practice advice and is intended to supplement any contractual requirements, consultation with regulators or company procedures rather than replace them.

Acknowledgments

Research project

This publication was produced as a result of CIRIA Research Project 708, "Control of water pollution from linear construction projects" and was written by Ms Emma Murnane and Mr Andy Heap of Hyder Consulting Ltd and Mr Andrew Swain of Edmund Nuttall Ltd.

CIRIA managers

The project was initially developed by Ms Marianne Scott and subsequently managed by Dr Das Mootanah, and Ms Victoria Cole, CIRIA.

Steering group

CIRIA would like to express its thanks and appreciation to all members of the project steering group for their contributions:

Chairman	Dr Nick O'Riordan	Arup
Members	Dr Paul Beckwith	British Waterways
	Mr Barry Beecroft	The BOC Foundation
	Mr Martin Brock	Balfour Beatty
	Mr Phil Chatfield	Environment Agency
	Mr Ian Clarke	Morgan Est
	Mr Peter Fisher	Costain Ltd
	Mr Dave Gibson	Alfred McAlpine
	Mr Sam Hall	Carillion
	Ms Sarah Hides	Defra
	Mr Gareth Jones	MJ Gleeson Group plc
	Mr Howell Jones	Amec Group Ltd.
	Mr Peter Martin	Black and Veatch
	Ms Liz McDonnell	Defra
	Mr Grahame Newman	British Waterways
	Mr Simon Price	Highways Agency
	Mr Stan Redfearn	The BOC Foundation

Acknowledgements

	Mr Will Rogers	URS Corporation
	Mr S Santhalingam	Highways Agency
	Dr Mike de Silva	Transport for London
	Dr Steve Yeoman	National Grid Transco
Corresponding members	Mr John Lonergan	Balfour Beatty
	Mr Alistair McNeill	Scottish Environment Protection Agency
	Ms Elizabeth Morrison	Scottish Executive

Funders

The project was funded by The BOC Foundation, the Highways Agency, Defra, the Environment Agency and the Scottish Executive.

Contents

CIRIA C649

Abstraction	Removal of water from surface water or groundwater, usually by pumping.
Aquifer	A source of groundwater comprising water-bearing rock, sand or gravel capable of yielding significant quantities of water.
Balancing pond	Pond or lagoon where the outflow is restricted to a steady rate and the inflow varies. Often used to control runoff and prevent flooding – see also settlement pond.
Bund	A barrier, dam or mound used to contain or exclude water (or other liquids). Can either refer to a bund made from earthworks material, sand etc or to a metal/concrete structure surrounding, for example, a fuel tank.
Contaminated land	Non-legislative definition: land with elevated concentrations of hazardous substances that either occur naturally or, more often, result from past or current industrial activities and present an actual or potential hazard to human health and/or the environment.
Controlled waters	Almost all natural waters in the UK are controlled waters. They include rivers, streams, ditches, ponds and groundwater. Termed waterways in Northern Ireland.
Dewatering	The removal of groundwater/surface water to lower the water table or to empty an area, such as an excavation, of water.
Discharge consent	Permission to discharge effluent, subject to conditions laid down in the consent, issued by the relevant environmental regulator.
Ecology	All living things, such as trees, flowering plants, insects, birds and mammals, and the habitats in which they live.

Glossary

Environmental impact assessment A technique used for identifying the environmental effects of development projects.

Outfall End of a temporary or permanent pipeline from which water (or other effluent) is discharged. Can refer to a dedicated structure or simply to the end of a length of pipe.

Pipejacking Method for directly installing pipes by hydraulic or other jacking from a driveshaft such that the pipes form a continuous string in the ground.

Pollution The introduction of a substance that has the potential to cause harm to the environment. Pollutants include silty water, oils, chemicals, litter and mud.

Risk assessment A process requiring an evaluation of the risk that may arise from identified hazards, combining the various factors contributing to the risk and then estimating their significance.

Runoff Runoff is a term used to describe the water from rain, snowmelt or irrigation that flows over the land surface and is not absorbed into the ground, instead flowing into streams or other surface waters or land depressions.

Sediment General term describing particles such as soil, sand, clay, silt and mud. It is the main water pollutant from construction. See suspended solids.

Settlement tank/pond Pond, tank or lagoon used to hold water in order to reduce turbulence thus allowing solid particles to settle out. See also balancing pond.

Sump A hole or pit that may be lined or unlined and is used to collect water to enable pumping out.

Surface water sewer Sewer system carrying surface water runoff from hardstanding, roads and building roofs etc.

CIRIA C649

Suspended solids	General term describing particles such as sand, clay, silt, mud or other sediment in suspension in water. Used as a water quality indicator.
Unsaturated zone	The zone between the ground surface and the water table.
Watercourse	A natural or artificial linear structure that transports water (river, canal, culvert etc).

Abbreviations

COSHH	Control of Substances Hazardous to Health Regulations 2002 (SI 2002/2677)
Defra	Department for Environment, Food and Rural Affairs
DTI	Department of Trade and Industry
EA	Environment Agency [England and Wales]
EHS	Environment and Heritage Service [Northern Ireland]
ENDS	Environmental Data Services
ES	environmental statement
GBRs	General Binding Rules
IBC	intermediate bulk container
pH	measure of acidity (pH less than 7) or alkalinity (pH more than 7)
PPG	Pollution Prevention Guideline
RUSLE	revised universal soil loss equation
SEPA	Scottish Environment Protection Agency
SUDS	sustainable drainage system

This guide is written for use by construction personnel on site. It identifies the potential causes of water pollution that may arise from construction processes and provides guidance on the management and control of water on site. Chapters 1-4 provide guidance on what to consider before mobilising to site, Chapters 5 and 6 are specifically about general setting up and managing the site. The remaining chapters (7-13) identify the main issues that may arise on site and provide guidance on how to manage them. Figure 1 illustrates how these processes relate to each other.

This guide is accompanied technical guidance (CIRIA C648), which provides more information on all the following chapters, as well as detailed guidance on the project planning and design phase.

The approach and format of this guide matches that of other CIRIA site guides, eg C650 *Environmental good practice on site* (second edition) and SP151 *Site safety handbook*. Throughout the text, important information has been highlighted with the use of bullet points and text boxes. The following symbols have been used to help identify the types of information being provided:

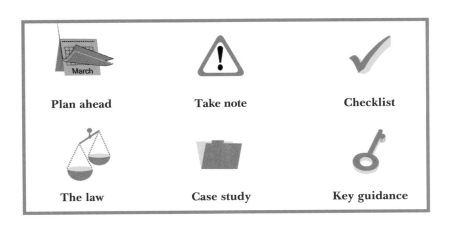

Plan ahead	**Take note**	**Checklist**
The law	**Case study**	**Key guidance**

How to use this guide

Table 1 lists the environmental regulatory authorities and their responsibilities with regard to the water environment.

Table 2 links a range of construction activities with water pollution issues. Select a construction activity from the left-hand column, look across the table to find which chapters will provide you with a chapter reference for the guidance you need. For major construction activities, eg tunnelling, there will be a range of supporting activities, eg dewatering. Information is prioritised by important guidance (p) and additional guidance (l) to assist finding key information quickly.

Note: Emergency and contingency planning (Chapter 4) is relevant to ALL activities on site.

Table 1   *Statutory authorities*

Statutory authority	Interest in water environment
Environmental regulators Environment Agency Scottish Environment Protection Agency Environment and Heritage Service	Flood defence and drainage Abstraction Water quality (surface and groundwater) Navigation Fisheries
Rivers Agency (Northern Ireland)	Drainage Flood defence Ecology
Local water company and sewerage undertaker	Water supply Disposal of trade effluent/sewage
Nature conservation bodies Natural England (formerly English Nature) Environment and Heritage Service Scottish Natural Heritage Countryside Council for Wales	Conservation
Internal drainage boards	Land drainage
British Waterways	Landowner Navigation and amenity Water quality Abstraction Ecology
Port authorities and harbour authorities	Landowner Navigation Commercial and amenity use
Defra (England and Wales) Fisheries Research Services (Scottish Executive)	Tidal areas Water quality Navigation

Table 2

Legend: ● = Important guidance; ▲ = Additional guidance.
Note: Emergency and Contingency Planning (Chapter 4) is relevant to ALL activities on site.

	1 Site planning	2 Licences and consents	3 Monitoring	5 Site set-up	6 Adjacent land and water use	7 Runoff and sediment control	8 Water treatment and disposal	9 Works in or near water	10 Excavations and dewatering	11 Concrete and grouting activities	12 Contaminated land	13 Ecology
Abstraction	●	▲	▲	●	●		●		▲		●	
Bridges	▲	▲	●			▲		▲	●	●		●
Chemicals				▲								
Cofferdams	▲	▲	●				▲	▲	▲	●		●
Commissioning project		▲					▲					●
Compounds, site	▲			▲	●							
Concrete, cement and grout				●			●	●		▲		
Culverts		▲	●				●	▲	●	●		●
Decommissioning/ demobilisation	●			●		▲						▲
Dewatering	●	▲	▲		●		▲		▲		●	
Directional drilling	●	▲					●	▲		▲	●	
Drainage works			●	●	▲	▲	●					
Dredging works	●	▲	●					▲			●	▲
Earthworks	●			●		▲			▲		▲	
Flood defences and bank works	●	▲	●			●		▲				▲
Floodplain, works in/on	▲					▲		▲				●
Fuel storage and refuelling				▲			●	●				
Haul route				▲	●	▲		●				●
Live systems	▲		●		●		●					
Material storage				▲		▲					●	
Monitoring/testing water	▲	●	▲				●		●			
Piling	●							●		▲	▲	
Pipejacking	●	▲					●	▲		▲	●	
Plant storage/maintenance				▲		●						
Reinstatement	●			●		▲						▲
Stockpiles				●		▲					●	
Topsoil stripping	▲					▲			▲			
Tunnelling	●	▲					●	▲		▲	●	
Vegetation stripping	▲					▲	▲	▲				
Waste		●		▲			▲					
Watercourse crossing near or over	▲	▲	●				●		▲			●
Water discharge/disposal	●	▲	▲		●		▲		●			
Water treatment	●	▲		●	●	●	▲					

Figure 1.1   Construction processes

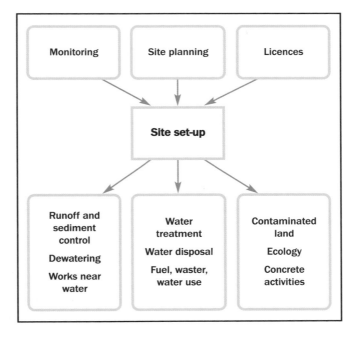

1   Site planning and programming

Planning linear construction projects is similar to any other project but with the additional need to take into account remote working areas, varying phases of construction and differing requirements along the route. Start by identifying the risks to surface water and groundwater. Focusing on high-risk areas will assist in the overall planning of the site layout, compounds and highlight the need for pollution prevention and control measures.

Put in place appropriate project environmental plans, procedures and method statements to manage the works effectively.

Careful planning and programming of construction works can greatly reduce the risks of watercourse pollution and delays in construction.

Risk assessment and control

1   Identify the location of all rivers, ponds, streams, aquifers, boreholes, field drains, fisheries, ecologically sensitive sites, surface and foul drainage systems on site and off site or downstream.

2   Mark these water bodies on a site plan to help plan the site set-up (eg storage areas, refuelling points, haul routes and washout areas).

3   Establish the baseline status of water features (flow, water quality etc).

4   Identify construction activities and sources of pollution that may affect the water bodies identified such as piling, dewatering, runoff, river crossings, fuel storage and concrete use.

5   Evaluate the risk of the construction activities causing pollution.

6   Remove or reduce the risks by:

   • using a different construction method or less hazardous materials

   • controlling the construction method, providing adequate bunding of fuel and other storage areas, installing measures such as diversion ditches and/or silt fences to control runoff

   • providing protection of the water body such as hardstanding for storage areas over sensitive groundwater, leaving grass unstripped along a river bank to filter runoff, and/or obtaining necessary permissions from environmental regulators.

Site management

Define the environmental responsibilities of site staff and subcontractors. Make site staff aware of particularly sensitive areas, high-risk activities, the implications of pollution and their roles and responsibilities. Provide site training in the form of site inductions, method statement briefings or toolbox talks for all staff and subcontractors. Subcontractors are strictly liable for any pollution they cause, but main contractors can also be prosecuted for allowing it.

Communication

Contact the environmental regulator and other regulatory authorities as early as possible to discuss the project and advise them of the activities taking place. There are several environmental regulators, each dealing with a different aspect of the water environment (see Table 1). Other stakeholders, such as landowners and water users downstream, should also be consulted at an early stage.

Seasonal constraints

Rainfall is far higher in northern and western parts of the UK than in the southern and eastern areas. You will need to consider seasonal weather variations in the works programme to minimise delays and pollution risks from heavy rainfall. Some activities, such as river crossings, may have to be postponed until the summer months, although where the watercourse has high amenity value restrictions may also be imposed on work during peak holiday periods.

Temporary works, on-site water treatment methods (ie settlement ponds) and other pollution prevention measures need to be designed at the outset to accommodate seasonal and local variations in rainfall and a worst-case flood scenario (a 1 in 10-year event is recommended).

Certain plant, animal and bird species that live in the water environment are legally protected. Formal consent is required for works in water and works affecting protected species and habitats. Restrictions may be placed on the timing of survey and construction works, eg to avoid breeding seasons.

Winterisation – road salt and de-icing

- cover stores of de-icing agents and ensure they drain to the foul sewer – obtain prior written permission from the statutory sewerage undertaker

- get up-to-date weather forecasts to avoid unnecessary use of de-icing agents and apply road salt at the rates specified by the Highways Agency

  Pre-salting $10–20$ g/m²

  After frost, ice or snow $20–40$ g/m²

- keep records of all de-icer use and review application method to minimise the amount of de-icing agent used

- take additional precautions over vulnerable or protected groundwater.

Site planning

1   Establish project organisation, environmental plans, method statements.

2   Identify water features, drains, downstream water users and other receptors and assess potential risks.

3   Confirm water quality baseline and identify suitable risk control measures.

4   Contact regulators, statutory bodies and other key stakeholders.

5   Establish project roles and environmental responsibilities at all work sites.

6   Identify any constraints on programming.

7   Provide site training for all personnel including subcontractors.

8   Prepare emergency and contingency plans and make all personnel aware of them (see Chapter 4).

The law requires you to have certain licences, consents and permission to protect the water environment. Before pumping any water, using a water supply, disposing of foul or surface water or working anywhere in or near water, check which written agreements you may need from the environmental regulator or the sewerage undertaker and make sure they are in place.

Once you have a consent or licence, make sure you comply with any conditions that are stated. These may be in the form of volume, quality, rate, timing restrictions or other requirements.

Check and monitor the discharge or works to ensure they are compliant. Maintain a record of these checks – you may need to use them in your defence in the event of a complaint or a pollution incident.

Checklist – licences and consents

1. Before starting work, decide whether your activities require a licence or consent (see table below).

2. Apply to the environmental regulator or sewerage undertaker. Make sure you plan early – some consents can take up to four months to obtain.

3. Comply with any conditions on programming, methodology, water quality, volume etc.

4. Monitor the works.

Activity	Licence and consent requirements
Disposal to sewer	Discharges to public foul sewer require **written permission** from the statutory sewage undertaker. In most cases, you should apply to your local water company (in England and Wales), Scottish Water (in Scotland) and the Water Service (in Northern Ireland).
Discharge into any surface water including a ditch, stream, river, lake or canal	Requires a **discharge consent** from the Environment Agency in **England** and **Wales**. If you are abstracting water (dewatering) before discharge you will need a **transfer licence** instead.
Discharge into groundwater	Requires one of three levels of **authorisation*** from the Scottish Environment Protection Agency (SEPA) in **Scotland**. Requires a **consent** from the Environment and Heritage Service (EHS) in **Northern Ireland**.
Temporary or permanent works in or over water	Requires a flood defence consent in **England** and **Wales**.
Works in the floodplain	In **Scotland**, building, engineering and other works in or in the vicinity of inland surface water and wetlands require one of the three levels of **authorisation*** from SEPA.
Works near a watercourse (within 10 m or more)	In **Northern Ireland**, if you intend to interfere with the flow of water in a watercourse (eg culverting) you should consult the Rivers Agency.
Dewatering groundwater	A **transfer licence** is likely to be required in **England** and **Wales** for overpumping and dewatering, where the water is not removed for use. An **abstraction licence** may be required to remove more than 20 m3 per day from surface water or groundwater for a specific use.
Pumping or abstracting groundwater or surface water	Note: If you are dewatering or pumping water that has collected in an excavation or shaft then you will not require an abstraction licence. If you intend using water from pumping or dewatering operations for dust suppression etc, you may then require an abstraction licence. In **Scotland** abstracting, dewatering and works in contact with groundwater require one of three levels of **authorisation*** from SEPA. In **Northern Ireland** you may need to obtain permission to abstract water from certain bodies of water, for instance when the source affects a protected habitat area.
Works in tidal waters	**Construction licences** are required for works in the tidal zone below mean high water springs in the **UK**. The licences are issued by departments within Defra, the Welsh Assembly Government, the Scottish Executive or the Northern Ireland Environment and Heritage Service.
Storage of oil	All construction sites in **Scotland** are likely to need **authorisation*** from SEPA for fuel storage on site.

* Note: There are three levels of **authorisation** in **Scotland**: general binding rules (GBRs), which cover specified low-risk activities; registration, which applies to activities with a predictable risk; and licences for activities with greater risk. Applications are required for registration and licences.

Monitoring is essential to demonstrate whether or not construction activities are having a detrimental impact on water quality and quantity. It is also used to identify off-site sources of pollution and to check compliance with licences and consents.

> Where detailed surveys are not required in the ES, planning or contract documentation, it is always worth carrying out baseline pre-construction monitoring of water quality.

Use a risk-based approach to determine what and where to monitor, based on the construction activities, the length of the project and the sensitivity of the location. Monitoring should be appropriate to the level of risk identified. Discuss and agree a monitoring regime with the environmental regulator.

Monitoring can include:

- water quality
- water level
- flow rate
- ecological surveys.

Monitoring records should include:

1   Staff member.
2   Date.
3   Time.
4   Weather conditions, recent and current.
5   Monitoring results or observations.
6   Ongoing construction activities (where appropriate).
7   Actions required (where necessary).

Water monitoring may be a requirement of an environmental statement, contract documents or discharge consent etc and can be carried out before, during and after construction, and particularly after a pollution incident.

Visual inspection

The simplest monitoring technique is visual inspection. Inspect water bodies and outfalls at regular intervals depending on the activities taking place:

- observe colour, smell, oily sheen, litter
- check that items of equipment such as flow meters are working correctly
- check whether straw bales, oil absorbents or other pollution controls need replacing
- measure water levels

- observe dust in the air or settling on water surface
- measure groundwater levels in boreholes/piezometers.

While records of visual inspections are very useful and demonstrate good practice, they are not adequate for demonstrating compliance with discharge or abstraction consents. Nevertheless, they can be used in addition to regular sample analysis.

On-site analysis

On-site kits are available for basic chemical tests and give almost immediate results. Typical kits include litmus papers (for pH), flow meters, oxygen meters and portable sample kits with reagents for a range of substances. Follow the supplier's advice and the instructions accompanying the equipment.

Laboratory analysis

The most costly, and most accurate, method of monitoring is sample collection and laboratory analysis. Always contact the lab before taking any samples, so it can provide appropriate containers and advise on the required tests, storage arrangements and transport. Seek specialist advice for detailed or long-term monitoring.

Ecological surveys can only be undertaken at certain times of the year. Qualified ecologists must be appointed to carry out surveys, and a licence may be required.

> Always undertake a health and safety risk assessment before inspecting or monitoring over or near water

Monitoring

1   Review the ES, planning consent and/or contract documents to identify any requirements for monitoring or surveys of surface water, groundwater or aquatic ecology and produce a monitoring programme.

2   Where no such requirement exists, identify any sensitive water receptors at or adjacent to the site that may be affected by the construction works.

3   Undertake baseline pre-construction monitoring of water quality, flow, water levels and/or ecology. Check the timing of the latter.

4   Monitor or inspect critical areas (eg outfalls, at watercourse crossings, boreholes) and compliance points (eg consented discharges).

5   Undertake monitoring before and after particular construction activities such as watercourse crossings.

6   Maintain records of all visual inspections, monitoring and laboratory analysis.

7   Review the monitoring results and take action where necessary to improve water quality, repair equipment and replace water treatment measures (oil booms etc).

8   Carry out post-construction monitoring, where required.

4   Emergency and contingency planning

The best way to manage pollution incidents is to prevent them. Assess all possible risks to the water environment and put measures in place to control the risks. Develop emergency procedures – project-specific, site-specific or activity-specific – and ensure that everyone on site knows them.

Checklist for action

1   Assess the pollution risks and develop an emergency response plan for the project or for each work location. Include details of site drainage, outfalls and watercourses so you know where pollution may end up.

2   Display a simple spill response procedure on site, at river crossings, near outfalls etc. It should include:

- an instruction to stop work and to switch off sources of ignition

- an instruction to contain the spill

- the location of spill clean-up materials

- the name and contact details of responsible staff to be notified

- measures particular to that location or activity (eg close pond outlet).

3   Obtain details of key people you may need to contact for help, eg radio/mobile contacts, out of hours, environmental regulator, water authorities and downstream water users (eg fish farm).

4   Provide equipment for dealing with pollution incidents.

5   Train staff to follow procedures and use equipment correctly.

6   Test the emergency plan regularly, and always after an incident.

7   Take action following an incident to ensure it does not occur again.

Emergency equipment – obtain from a reputable (UKSPILL-accredited) supplier and train site staff in its correct use. Use material safety data sheets and COSHH assessments for advice on appropriate spill measures	
Oil-absorbent granules ("cat litter")	Use only ON LAND. Oil floats on water – granules will not work because they sink
Floating booms	Tubes of material that contain solids or absorb oils and fuel in/on WATER. Fix with wooden stakes
Absorbent pads	Ideal for use in WATER, including drip trays and bunds that can fill with rainwater; can also be used on LAND
Polythene sacks	For disposal of used clean-up materials. Double-bag and/or store in appropriate container before disposal as hazardous waste
Straw bales	For use in filtering silt and coarser solids from flowing water
Geotextile sheeting	Can be used either to wrap straw bales to filter out fines or to line a temporary straw bale settlement facility
Drain covers	Specially designed covers that form a watertight seal when placed over storm drains
Timber planks	Useful as skimmer boards in ditches with slow-flowing water (to trap floating materials and oils/fuel)
Ropes or wooden stakes	For fixing absorbent booms (see Floating booms above)
Putty	To seal damaged drums

Site set-up – summary checklist

1   Be aware of restrictions on compound areas as identified in the contract documents, environmental statement, planning consent etc.

2   Assess the risk of all compound locations and draw up a drainage plan.

3   Select locations near existing facilities where possible, for example foul drainage, water supply, hardstanding.

4   Locate compounds away from watercourses (including ditches), low spots and aquifers.

5   Avoid locations that are designated conservation areas.

6   Identify areas with permitted access by public main road (reducing the need for haul roads).

7   Consider a sustainable water supply and minimise water use on site.

8   Provide adequate measures to control runoff from compounds and haul routes.

9   Obtain agreement for wastewater disposal.

10   Provide appropriate measures to secure the site and hazardous materials from vandals and trespassers.

11   Store fuel, oil and materials securely and in accordance with legal requirements.

Site drainage and water features

Prepare a drainage plan for the scheme, illustrating all surface water bodies and drainage systems within a 500 m-wide corridor of the route:

- rivers and streams
- field drains
- foul and surface water drains and outfalls
- ditches (including dry ones)
- canals and leats
- lakes, lochs, ponds, reservoirs and wetlands.

> Colour code the drainage system:
> - surface water – blue
> - foul drainage – red.
>
> Mark on plans and on site with paint, or with painted stakes in areas where drains may become buried.

When working on existing drainage systems, put temporary measures in place at the outfall (or intersection with other drainage) to remove sediments and oil, such as a catch pit, sump, or a geotextile screen, or temporarily block or divert the pipe or culvert.

Where field drains are truncated by the scheme, intercept and divert flows (with permission) to the outfall in a controlled manner to avoid discharging water into the works. Be aware of any activities upstream (eg muck spreading, ploughing) that may cause pollution to enter land drains.

Implement measures to minimise and control runoff, eg by using permeable materials for low-risk compound areas or excavating ditches either side of haul routes.

Water supply and use

1   Consult the water company, landowners and environmental regulator early on to source a sustainable supply of water for the site. Water supplies may be provided by a direct connection to a mains supply, a tanker or abstraction from local borehole or surface water. A licence is likely to be required for abstracting more than 20 m³/day. Licences may be seasonally restricted or not allowed at all in the south of the UK because of over-demand. Alternative solutions include transferring the licence from someone not using it or purchasing water from someone not using it (eg a licensed farm supply).

2   Obtain the necessary permissions and licences for a water supply and for its disposal.

3   Whatever the water source, it is likely that a charge will be made for the volume of water used, and ultimately the volume disposed. Use mains water for drinking water only. Conserve water where possible:

●   when cleaning concrete lorries, clean the chute only, using the smallest volume of water necessary. The remainder of cleaning should be done at the batching plant and the washout water recycled where possible. Use water from settlement ponds or similar facilities where possible

●   commercially available wheelwashes with efficient water recycling use less water and so cost less to operate

●   where a manned jet wash or lance spray is used, wash the vehicles in a bunded area where runoff can be contained and channelled to a treatment area, such as a settlement pond, prior to discharge

●   water from settlement ponds can be used to keep haul roads and site compounds damp to prevent dust

●   implement SUDS techniques such as settlement ponds, swales or greywater recycling to manage surface runoff where site offices and compounds are established for longer periods.

4   Obtain permission to use water for commissioning new pipelines, and for disposal of the water afterwards.

Wastewater disposal

Where mains sewerage is available, locate welfare facilities in an appropriate part of the site and connect them to the sewerage system. Agreement from the sewerage undertaker will be required. Where mains sewerage is not available, or where the compound is small and/or temporary, install cesspools, septic tanks or package plants with appropriate discharge with agreement from the environmental regulator (see PPG4 *Disposal of sewage where no mains drainage is available*).

Ordering, handling and storing materials

1   Consider whether the use of potentially polluting materials can be eliminated from the construction process or whether alternative materials that are more environmentally considerate can be used, eg biodegradable oils.

2   Can processes be undertaken elsewhere at less sensitive locations, for example, off site?

3   Check stock requirements – can smaller quantities be stored on site or delivered to site when they are needed?

4   Identify how materials will arrive so that the appropriate arrangement for handling and storage can be made.

5   Ensure deliveries are supervised at all times.

6   Store materials in accordance with manufacturers' requirements.

7   Store materials well away from sensitive receptors – at least 50 m from a spring or borehole and 10 m from a watercourse or drain.

8   Store materials on a level, impermeable base – concrete slab or other hardstanding.

9   Store materials away from vehicle movements.

10 Consider the consequences of extreme weather conditions for material storage.

11 Provide appropriate containment for hazardous materials and waste.

12 Maintain an up-to-date inventory of products or materials stored.

13 Provide waste storage areas at all work sites where possible. See Site waste management plans. Guidance for construction contractors and clients; <www.dti.gov.uk/construction/sustain/site_waste_management.pdf>).

Fuel and oil

The Control of Pollution (Oil Storage) (England) Regulations 2001 are applicable to any oil container with a storage capacity of 200 litres or more. A 45 gallon drum = 205 litres.

The regulations apply to England. Contractors working in Wales, Scotland and Northern Ireland are advised to comply with these good practice requirements as similar legislation is being considered across the UK. In summary the regulations require:

- containers to be bunded or placed on a drip tray (Figure 5.1)
- bunds must be capable of storing 110 per cent of the capacity (or 25 per cent of combined capacity of drums and other containers)
- refuelling hoses, vent pipes, delivery pipes and sight gauges must be contained within the bund
- dispensing nozzles or taps must be locked shut when not in use.

See also PPG2 *Above ground oil storage tanks*, PPG8 *Storage and disposal of used oils* and PPG26 *Storage and handling of drums and intermediate bulk containers* (IBCs).

Figure 5.1   *Fuel storage site guidelines* (courtesy Nuttall)

Rainwater in bunds and drip trays

The volume of rainwater should not exceed 5 per cent of the total capacity of a bund or drip tray. Rainwater can be discharged to foul sewer or to ground provided no oily sheen is visible. Small quantities of oil can be removed from the surface of the water using oil-absorbent pads (NOT granules) or water can be poured from drip trays etc through a pad before disposal. Where the oil/water mix cannot be separated fully the liquid needs to be removed and stored prior to disposal by a specialist waste management contractor.

Biodegradable oils must be stored handled and disposed of as any other oil and must not be disposed to surface water or foul drains.

Fuel and oils

1   Assess the risks of potential fuel and oil storage areas.

2   Establish fuel and oil stores in line with the Control of Pollution (Oil Storage) (England) Regulations 2001.

3   Train operatives for refuelling plant, equipment and the application of oil-based products.

4   Bring plant and equipment to a designated refuelling area rather than refuelling them at numerous locations about the site where possible.

5   Use integrally bunded mobile bowsers where necessary; impose strict controls on vehicle speed limits; be aware of rutted, muddy ground to avoid overturning; provide a temporary bridge or culverted crossing in preference to regular fording of a watercourse.

6   Develop emergency procedures for dealing with spills and tell the workforce about them; keep a stock of absorbent materials such as sand, spill granules and absorbent pads at each work site, on plant, and particularly at refuelling and storage areas.

7   Regularly inspect and maintain oil stores, bunds and drip trays.

Site security

Contractors can be liable for environmental damage caused by intruders and vandals if they have not made reasonable attempts to guard against it. This liability may increase if vandals have previously struck at a site.

Fencing – post and rail fencing (which can be part of the permanent works) may be installed to denote the site boundary, while more secure fencing can be used around the site office and compound areas.

Access – strict controls on access and the movement of people on site can help reduce incidents of trespass and theft. Measures that should be considered include site passes, security guards and supervising visitors and deliveries.

Protect **plant and equipment** from unauthorised use with locking devices, parking up plant close together at the end of shifts, returning heavy plant to the main compound at weekends and storing high-risk equipment out of sight in lockable containers

Storage of materials – avoid storing materials against site boundaries and fencing as they can provide a means for thieves and vandals to access site. All potentially hazardous materials should be stored securely in accordance with COSHH requirements.

Signage – display warning notices around the site perimeter and on the approach to site compound areas to deter potential intruders.

Site security lighting is a good deterrent to vandals and thieves, but it can also cause nuisance to local residents. Keep site lighting at the minimum brightness to provide adequate security and safety and angled away from residential properties.

Emergency incidents – emergency procedures (see Chapter 4) should actions required in the event of vandalism causing pollution and contact names/numbers outside normal working hours. All site personnel, including security personnel, need to be briefed on these arrangements.

A contractor was fined £4000 for polluting a river with gas oil following vandalism of an oil tank on site (*The ENDS Report*)

A linear site is likely to occupy a narrow strip of land and to have many neighbours, not just either side but also upstream and downstream along watercourses and drainage networks.

 Surface water and groundwater will not recognise the site boundary and will continue to flow both into and away from the site works.

Find out from the ES who uses the land, surface water and groundwater around and downstream of the site. Discussion with the environmental regulator, conservation bodies and often local employees can be helpful too. Be aware of any sensitive uses (which may be some distance from the site), such as:

Surface water	Groundwater
Fishery Water abstraction – farm, water company, industrial Public recreation area Protected site or species	Private or industrial supply borehole Aquifer or protected groundwater Ponds and other surface waters affected by groundwater level Wetland

Checklist – adjacent land and water use

1   Be aware of any sensitive users of land, surface water or groundwater around the site, particularly downstream. Contact landowners/occupiers to understand their interests and advise them what is being done to protect them where appropriate.

2   Be aware of any off-site and upstream sources of pollution, even some distance away, which may include land contamination, farming activities and other construction work. Confirm who is responsible for off-site pollution, such as agricultural runoff, that may be released through "your" outfall.

3   Put in place measures to protect the works where possible from any likely off-site pollution (eg diversion ditches, bunds).

4   Implement pollution prevention procedures to protect the surrounding area and water users (eg correct working methods, treatment of water prior to disposal with appropriate regulatory consent).

5   Consider what may happen in the event of heavy rainfall, flooding or a pollution incident on an adjacent site and have a contingency plan.

6   Identify areas of adjacent land that may be suitable for discharging small volumes of silty water to allow it to infiltrate through the ground or to construct an emergency temporary settlement pond.

7   Monitor the works and keep records of observations on and off site. These records may help in the event of a complaint or a prosecution.

Sediment, including all soils, mud, clay, silt, sand etc, is the single main pollutant generated at construction sites. It originates largely from the erosion of exposed soils by surface water runoff. Erosion control is intended to prevent runoff flowing across exposed ground and becoming polluted with sediments. Sediment control is designed to slow runoff and thereby allow any suspended solids to settle out.

Once runoff becomes contaminated with sediment it is difficult and expensive to remove. In some cases a combination of erosion control and sediment control may be required.

Principles of erosion and sediment control

1   Erosion control is much more effective than sediment control in preventing water pollution.

2   Plan erosion and sediment controls early in the project and incorporate them into the works programme.

3   Install drainage and runoff controls BEFORE beginning site clearance and earthworks.

4   Prevent runoff from flowing on to the site over adjacent land or through field drains.

5   Minimise the area of exposed ground on site by stripping vegetation and topsoil only when needed, rather than well in advance.

6   Provide appropriate control and containment measures on site.

7   Monitor and maintain erosion and sediment controls throughout the project.

8   Establish vegetation as soon as possible on all exposed soil.

Preparing a runoff and sediment control plan

1   Use a site map, preferably topographic, to identify and illustrate existing land use, surface water, low-lying areas and natural drainage ways (which may be dry) on and adjacent to the site; include any protected or sensitive sites identified in the ES or other documentation.

2   Illustrate on the map the proposed construction activities most likely to have the potential for runoff, such as steep slopes, cuttings, embankments, stockpiles, haul roads.

3   Assess the potential for runoff, ponding of water and even flooding, by reviewing soil types, topography and rainfall data before starting work.

4   Select the best methods to reduce runoff and erosion for the site conditions.

5   Ensure that control measures are adequately sized and correctly installed. Initial runoff controls must be in place before site works begin.

6   Address additional source controls to reduce pollution in stormwater runoff including storage of equipment and materials, waste, water use and disposal.

7   Inspect control measures regularly and particularly after rainfall, to determine if the controls are working adequately or whether further measures are required.

Estimating rainfall and runoff

Rainfall events vary with season. Heavier short-period rainfall, such as that caused by thunderstorms, is usually expected in summer, whereas higher rainfall totals over periods of a day are more likely in winter. The rainfall that can be expected at any site in the UK can be estimated from mapped information (refer to the technical guidance, CIRIA C648).

Runoff volume depends on three main factors:

- catchment size and topography
- infiltration rates of the ground
- rainfall intensity and duration.

Select a probability of rainfall event that is appropriate to the construction timeframe and the risk of failure. A likely minimum design period for temporary works is once in 10 years, with an overspill contingency for greater events.

Identify areas along the scheme that are prone to flooding such as floodplains, low-lying areas, dry valleys or channels. Prepare detailed flood emergency and contingency plans including arrangements to make safe any static plant or compounds, move mobile plant and evacuate site operatives away from flood-affected areas. Sign up for fax or email forecasts from the Met Office's MetBuild Direct service at **<www.met-office.gov.uk/construction/mbdirect/index.html>** and register with the environmental regulator (such as <www.environment-agency.gov.uk/floodline>) to receive early warning by telephone or fax in certain areas.

> **In the event of a flood, the law states that taking all reasonable precautions against pollution is a defence in such an instance.**

Estimating sediment generation

The principal factors influencing erosion are:

- rainfall intensity (R)
- soil erodibility (K)
- slope gradient (S)
- slope length (L)
- any surface cover or treatment (CP).

> These have been combined within the revised universal soil loss equation (RUSLE).
>
> $$A = RK(LS)CP$$
>
> Refer to CIRIA C648 for details on using the equation.

Erosion and sediment controls

Leaving unstripped vegetation – across the site or in filter strips – is the simplest and the most effective way to prevent erosion. Once vegetation is cleared or the topsoil stripped, the exposed ground and resulting runoff must be controlled by other means.

Vegetation and topsoil stripping

1   Delay clearing and topsoil-stripping of each phase of works until shortly before construction begins rather than stripping the whole site many months before construction.

2   Leave as much existing vegetation as possible, protecting it during construction with fencing, signs etc.

3   Leave existing (or plant new) vegetation along the perimeter of the site, haul roads or stockpiles to provide an effective sediment filter.

4   Leave 5 m-wide grassed strip next to river banks to filter sediment, or place grassed soil bunds along river banks etc to prevent runoff reaching the watercourse.

5   Seed temporary stockpiles, embankments and graded areas as the work progresses. If there is no time to establish grass cover on a slope, even leaving the slope roughened will provide better erosion control than leaving it smooth. Alternatively, apply woodchip mulch or geotextile matting.

6   Close and stabilise open trenches as soon as possible. Sequence trenching projects so that most open portions of the trench are closed before new trenching is begun.

Mulching and binders

Mulches include straw, wood chips, bark and gravel and are used to temporarily and permanently stabilise or protect cleared or seeded areas. Mulch prevents erosion by protecting the soil surface and holding seeds, fertilisers and topsoil in place until growth occurs.

Binders are biodegradable adhesives that can be applied directly to the soil or over a layer of mulch. They are usually mixed with water and sprayed on. Seek advice from a supplier to select the appropriate mulch or binder and application method.

Geotextiles and mats

Meshes, netting, mats and sheeting made of natural or man-made material can be used to stabilise soil either temporarily or permanently. They can also be used outside the growing season when seeding would be unsuccessful. Jute, straw and other organic matting materials provide temporary protection until permanent vegetation is established and will not need to be removed, as they will rot down.

Design – geotextile and matting (Figure 7.1)

- apply by rolling down slope in direction of water flow

- overlap both edges

- make sure products are securely staked down

- where impermeable mats are used (eg plastic sheeting), provide a straw or rock I barrier or silt fence at the toe of the slope.

Figure 7.1   *Coconut matting and silt fence* (courtesy Oregon Department of Environmental Quality)

Haul roads and site access

 Efficient haul road stabilisation not only reduces erosion but can also significantly speed up works during bad weather.

Design – haul roads

- follow the contour of the natural ground as much as possible

- slope should not exceed 15 per cent

- grade haul roads to drain across rather than along; use low earth bunds to divert water off the haul road

- provide drainage ditches on each side (or on downslope side) of the haul road to channel water to a treatment area (settlement etc). Simple gravel banks without a trench can also be used to filter runoff

- if plant or vehicles have to make repeated crossings of a watercourse, erect a temporary haul road bridge or flumed/culverted crossing.

Site access to or from a public road should have a stabilised construction, consisting of aggregate underlain with geotextile fabric. Wheel-washing facilities may also be required where dirty trucks regularly leave the site.

Protection of stockpiles

To minimise the loss of sediment and pollution risk from stockpiles:

- locate them away from drains and watercourses
- seed or provide other stabilisation measures appropriate to the length of time stored
- provide earth bunds or other diversion to keep runoff away from stockpiles
- provide silt fences or straw/rock barriers at the toe of the stockpile to mitigate runoff during rain events.

Diversion drains

Diversion drains typically combine an earth bund and a ditch (or bund on its own) channelling runoff to a settlement pond or other stabilised area (Figure 7.3). They should be used:

- for channelling upslope runoff away from, across or around the site
- for channelling runoff downslope of the site to prevent it leaving the site
- around the toe of stockpiles or slopes
- at the top of slopes, channelling runoff to a slope drain (see below).

Figure 7.3   *Diversion drain alongside sloping pipeline easement* (courtesy Alfred McAlpine)

Slope drains

A slope drain is a temporary pipe or lined channel to drain the top of a slope to a stable discharge point at the bottom of a slope without causing erosion (Figure 7.4). Use rigid or flexible pipe, plastic sheet or geotextile anchored to the slope. Slope drains are used in conjunction with a diversion drain along the top edge of the slope, which directs water to an inlet at the top of the drain.

Figure 7.4   *Slope drain* (courtesy Oregon Department of Environmental Quality)

Check dams and sediment traps

These are small temporary dams constructed across a diversion ditch (NOT a natural watercourse) to slow down runoff and cause sedimentation behind the dam (Figure 7.5). If properly anchored, wood, straw bale or rock filter bunds may be used for check dams.

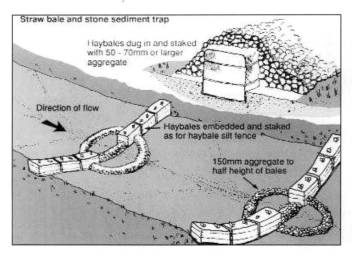

Straw bale and stone sediment trap

Haybales dug in and staked with 50 - 70mm or larger aggregate

Direction of flow

Haybales embedded and staked as for haybale silt fence

150mm aggregate to half height of bales

Figure 7.5   *Check dams* (courtesy Environment ACT)

Slope roughening

Rough slope surfaces may look unfinished, but they will erode less than smooth graded surfaces and will vegetate more quickly. If there is no time to establish grass cover on a slope, even covering the slope with topsoil will provide better erosion control than leaving the slope uncovered.

Silt fence

A silt fence comprises a geotextile filter fabric, straw bales or a combination of the two fixed to supporting posts along the edge of the site or around the toe of a cleared slope or stockpile (Figure 7.6). A silt fence will remove coarse particles, but is not as effective in removing very fine particles. The filter fabric must be entrenched at least 100 mm into the ground (commercially available fences have a printed indicator line for installation depth) and the ends turned uphill to prevent runoff around the fence.

Clear away accumulated silt regularly; commercially available silt fences have a printed indicator line above which silt should not accumulate.

Straw bales can also be used to filter out heavy sediments. During wet weather bales deteriorate rapidly and require frequent replacement, but are a cost-effective temporary measure. Greater efficiency can be achieved by wrapping straw bales in geotextile.

Figure 7.6   *Fabric silt fence at toe of stockpile* (courtesy International Erosion Control Association)

Protecting existing and pre-earthworks drainage

The main contractor can be held responsible for the quality of water flowing to an outfall used during construction. Identify the location of all existing surface water drains, sewers, manholes, field drains and pre-construction drainage. Prevent polluted water entering drains on site and be aware of any off-site sources.

Surface water drains

Where an existing surface water sewer system is present on or adjacent to the site (eg highway or railway drainage), protect the drain inlets with gravel or geotextile filters (Figures 7.7 and 7.8).

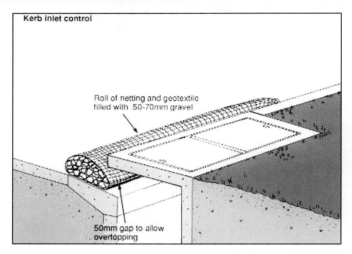

Figure 7.7   *Kerb inlet control*

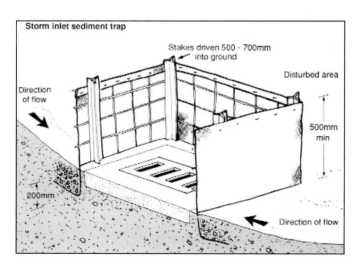

Figure 7.8   *Storm drain control* (both courtesy Environment ACT)

Land drains

Existing land (field) drains can be difficult to detect. During heavy rain land drains can potentially transport silt pollution from the site into watercourses. Locate the outfalls and monitor them. Make sure that land drainage can be isolated if necessary.

Where land drains are cut off they can discharge large volumes of water on to the site. Intercept and divert flows across the site to a suitable outfall.

Pre-earthworks drains

Seal the surface of the drains with clay to prevent ingress from silty runoff into the stone backfill, which would otherwise discharge to the watercourse without any treatment, causing pollution.

Sustainable drainage systems (SUDS)

Permanent SUDS are usually not designed for the sediment volumes generated during construction, so great care must be taken to ensure sediment does not enter any part of the system. Where permanent SUDS can be used during construction (eg balancing pond) then sediment should be cleaned out after the construction phase is completed.

All construction sites generate polluted wastewater, known as "trade effluent". This includes water generated in the following situations on site:

- surface water runoff (from compounds and areas stripped of vegetation etc)
- dewatering from excavations
- washing operations
- rainwater collected in drip trays and bunds
- road sweepers
- works in cofferdams
- wastewater from welfare facilities.

It is an offence to cause pollution (which includes silt, mud, concrete, diesel, oil, sewage, litter etc) to enter surface water or groundwater.

Proof that actual harm has been done is not required.

Trade effluent requires permission for its discharge or disposal and usually needs treatment if it is polluted. The only wastewater not regarded as trade effluent is clean surface runoff (ie from roofs) and clean water from groundwater dewatering.

In all cases, the first priority should be to control the source of pollution. The most common pollutants present in water on site are:

- sediment (suspended solids such as soil, mud, silt and clay)
- cement products
- hydrocarbons such as fuel and oil
- heavy metals
- organic wastes (sewage and welfare effluent).

Sediment

Silt is the main pollutant generated at construction sites. The first priority is to control the source by controlling runoff, dewatering or works in water. There are several ways to treat it.

Pumping to grassed land – infiltration

One simple method is to pump directly on to a grassy area. This approach is most suitable for small volumes pumped at intervals, for example dewatering an excavation at the start of each shift or dewatering a trench with slow water ingress. A more detailed method is to establish an infiltration basin. This is much the same as a settlement pond, but has no outfall to a watercourse, and relies on water infiltrating into the underlying ground (see Table 8.1).

Check for land drains before pumping water over the ground, as silty water will flow through them straight to a watercourse.

A construction company and an engineering company were each fined £15 000 after rivers in north-east Scotland were repeatedly polluted with silt from a construction project. More than 50 000 fish were killed, and one incident turned 20 km of a burn brown with muddy silt. SEPA traced the pollution to the pipeline construction work. In sinking the pipeline, silt-laden rainwater had to be pumped out of the workings. Instead of being disposed of safely, the contractors pumped it on to surrounding fields. The muddy water entered watercourses through field drains at several sites. Samples taken by SEPA showed silt levels 450 times above normal background levels.

Table 8.1   Typical infiltration rates for various soils

Soil texture	Sand	Sandy loam	Loam	Clay loam	Silty clay	Clay
Infiltration rate (mm/h)	50	25	13	8	3	5
Typical mm/h (range)	(25–250)	(13–75)	(8–20)	(3–15)	(0.3–5)	(1–10)
Typical l/min/ha*	8000	4000	2000	1300	500	800

* Assuming the water to be spread evenly over the surface (CIRIA C650).

Infiltration

1. Not suitable for oil, concrete and chemical contamination.

2. Not suitable where there is wet ground, land drains (unless they can be sealed or diverted), a shallow water table or protected groundwater areas.

3. Before pumping, seek permission from the landowner. If the area has sensitive groundwater you may also need approval from the environmental regulator.

4. Pump at a rate that will allow water to infiltrate the ground (Table 8.1).

5. Make sure water does not run overland and into nearby watercourses.

6. Move the outfall hose from time to time or use an agricultural "rainmaker" to avoid one area becoming saturated and vegetation being smothered. A typical agricultural sprayer discharges at about 1000 l/min.

Settlement ponds

To calculate the volume of runoff that can be anticipated refer to CIRIA C648.

Where a balancing pond forms part of the permanent works, construct it at the outset and use it to control and treat site water. The pond may require lining (with clay or a proprietary liner) to make it impermeable depending on the local geology. Seal land drains, upslope and downslope, where they cross the site, but make sure the land upslope will not become waterlogged or flooded as a result.

> When designing a pond select a probability of rainfall that is appropriate to the length of the project and the risk of failure. A likely minimum design period for temporary works is **once in 10 years**, with an overspill contingency for greater events.

Contractors must have consent to discharge from a settlement pond during construction, even if the pond is to be part of the permanent works (only permanent drainage may be exempt, eg under the Highways Act 1980).

The outfall should be placed as far away from the inlet(s) as possible. Outfall structures should always be checked and maintained. Long-term ponds (one year or more) may require management to prevent algal blooms, sediment build-up and excessive vegetation growth.

Settlement tanks

Settlement tanks are purpose-made structures that contain a series of baffles over which water flows. When installing settlement tanks to remove silt, ensure that the baffles are fixed at the bottom of the tank so that the water flows over them. Settlement tanks can also be set up using skips in series with v-notches for the outlet.

Size the pump rate and the tank correctly otherwise the tanks will not work (Table 8.2). If the water is churning in the tank then it will not be effective – aim for a slow flow.

Table 8.2   *Theoretical range of retention times for a variety of particle sizes*

Water depth	Retention time (settling velocity)				
	Fine clay (0.001 mm/s)	Fine silt (0.02 mm/s)	Medium silt (0.05 mm/s)	Coarse sand (30 mm/s)	Flocculated silt (10 mm/s)
0.5 m	6 days	7 h	3 h	16 s	50 s
1 m	11 days	14 h	5.5h	33 s	2 min
2 m	23 days	1 day	11 h	1 min	3 min

Specialist treatment equipment

Flocculating agents increase the rate of settlement of suspended solids by "pulling together" smaller particles into larger, and therefore heavier, particles.

Liquid flocculant is added to water in a tank or pond. Over a period of time (up to 24 hours) the particles come together and settle out (Figure 8.1).

Solid flocculant, usually in the form of "floc blocks", is designed to be placed in a channel of flowing water and dissolve in the flow, providing a dose of the chemical. The performance of the blocks is dependent on the flow and the suspended sediment concentration.

You must seek specialist advice on the design and use of any flocculant or coagulant system. You will also need approval from the relevant environmental regulator before using flocculants.

Separators – purpose-made equipment can separate several pollutants, including oils and solids, from site water.

Figure 8.1a　*Water sample 15 seconds after adding flocculant*

Figure 8.1b　*Water sample five minutes after adding flocculant*

Settlement facilities

1 Where retention ponds form part of the permanent works, construct them at the outset and use to control water during construction.

2 Check for land drains and seal or divert them.

3 Temporary ponds need to be designed for stormwater/flood events appropriate to the length of the project. A 1in 10-year storm event is recommended, with a contingency such as a spillway for major events.

4 Suspended solids will only settle out when the water is still. Size the pump rate and settlement tanks correctly; if the water is churning in a tank then it will not work effectively.

5 Suspended solids need time to settle (generally 2–3 hours, but finer material may take up to 15 hours), so several ponds or tanks in series may be needed.

6 Chemical flocculants are highly suitable for linear schemes where space is restricted. Seek specialist advice and regulatory permission before using them.

Filtration

Filtration uses the flow of water, rather than keeping it still, to remove sediments. There are two methods. First, there are techniques used to trap sediment as runoff is flowing across site or along channels (see Chapter 7).

The second is filtration by pumping water through steel tanks or skips filled with a suitable filter, such as fine single-size aggregate (5–10 mm), geotextile or straw bales. It is an easy and cheap option, suitable for treating discharges with fairly coarse particles.

Concrete and cementitious materials

Treatment options will depend on the volume of water and the availability and treatment of other water on site:

- settle-out concrete solids from washout operations in a skip or lagoon
- pump water from washout areas into the on-site batching plant if there is one

- prior to disposal make sure the settled water meets any discharge consent conditions for pH (alkalinity/acidity) either by dilution with other water on site or by chemical dosing (seek specialist advice).

Fuel, oil and other hydrocarbons

Prevent fuel and oil from entering the water environment. Oil-polluted water generated in site runoff, and in particular from fuel bunds, drip trays and refuelling areas, can be treated by using:

- oil separators to remove hydrocarbons at high-risk areas of runoff
- oil-absorbent pads or booms floated on the water surface in the event of a fuel spill or to clean up small quantities of oil.

Sewage

Never discharge sewage to the ground or to a surface water drain or watercourse. All sewage and wastewater should go to the foul sewer, septic tanks or package plants with permission from the sewerage undertaker and environmental regulator.

Metals

Metals often adhere to sediment particles and are removed via sedimentation, filtration or similar sediment removal process. Chemical additives can be used to settle out metals dissolved in water. Seek specialist advice and approval from the environmental regulator before using chemicals or disposing of metal-polluted sediments.

Ammonia and oxygen

Where water quality is poor due to lack of oxygen or high ammonia, the water should be aerated using weirs, commercial bubble diffusers, compressors or aerators.

Disposal options

Before discharging any water, ensure that permission has been obtained to do so. Select from the following prioritised options:

- infiltrate as near to source as possible (see Sediment – infiltration, above)
- discharge to a local watercourse, with written permission from the environmental regulator
- connect to sewer, with written permission from the statutory sewerage undertaker
- dispose of as "controlled waste" in accordance with the Environmental Impact (Duty of Care) Regulations 1991.

Practical considerations for water disposal

- the volumes of water involved, based on the size and characteristics of the site and catchment
- site topography (to determine where water will collect, and whether pumping is required)
- inclusion of features such as balancing ponds in permanent design
- Whether space is available for temporary storage and treatment
- location of suitable receiving water
- location of the connection to the foul sewer
- degree and type of any pollution
- agreement from the environmental regulator or sewerage undertaker (formal permission will be required)
- the charges to be levied by the regulator and sewerage undertaker.

Activity	Licence and consent requirements
Discharge to sewer	Discharges to public foul sewer anywhere in UK require **written permission** from the statutory sewage undertaker
Pumping into any surface water	Requires a consent from the Environment Agency (**England and Wales**), SEPA (**Scotland**) or the Environment and Heritage Service (**Northern Ireland**), in addition to any permission to work in water or near water, and to abstract
Pumping to ground or groundwater	

> Consents for discharges to surface water and sewers can take up to four months to obtain, so plan early. Ensure the discharges comply with all conditions given in the discharge consents by monitoring them.

Outfalls

Protect the banks and bed of watercourses from scouring at or opposite the outfall by using baffles, an energy dissipater, geotextile, stone or plastic sheet. Provide safe access to allow sampling and monitoring of the discharge, either at the outfall itself or via a manhole.

A flow restrictor and/or a flow meter may need to be installed to limit and/or monitor the flow rate to that allowed in the discharge consent. Provide some method to close or isolate the outfall in the event of a pollution incident.

Water treatment and disposal

1   Consider pollution prevention measures before water treatment measures.

2   Review the site characteristics (topography, watercourses, foul sewers) and construction activities to determine where you will need to dispose of water.

3   Consider the priorities: (i) infiltration, (ii) discharge to watercourse, (iii) discharge to sewer.

4   Apply for consents from the sewerage undertaker and environmental regulator.

5   Select appropriate treatment method depending on the pollution, the required water quality for discharge and the available space.

6   Manage the use of water to reduce the volume requiring disposal.

7   Minimise erosion and scour by providing an adequate, accessible outfall.

8   Set up measures to monitor the discharge.

Activity	Licence and consent requirements (see also Chapter 2)
Pumping into any surface water including a ditch, stream, river, lake or canal	Requires a licence from the Environment Agency (England and Wales), one of three levels of authorisation from SEPA (Scotland) or consent from the Environment and Heritage Service (Northern Ireland), in addition to any permission to work in water or near water, and to abstract.
Temporary or permanent works in or over water	Requires consent from the Environment Agency (England and Wales) or one of three levels of authorisation from SEPA (Scotland), in addition to any permission to abstract or discharge water. In Northern Ireland consult the Rivers Agency.
Works in the floodplain	A licence will be required from the Environment Agency (England and Wales) for pumping more than 20 m³/day; or one of three levels of authorisation is required from SEPA (Scotland), in addition to any permission to work in water and discharge water. In Northern Ireland consult the Environment and Heritage Service.
Works near a watercourse (within 10 m or more)	
Abstracting surface water (dewatering, overpumping)	

Key guidance

PPG5 *Works in, near or liable to affect watercourses*

If British Waterways owns or manages the waterway (particularly canals) its Code of practice for works affecting British Waterways (<**www.britishwaterways.co.uk/images/COP_2005.pdf**>) must be followed.

1.   At an early stage discuss the works and obtain the required consents from the environmental regulator, British Waterways and/or the internal drainage board.

2.   Assess the pollution risks of the works and mitigate the risks at source wherever possible.

3.   Prepare a detailed method statement (one will be required for consent applications) including pollution prevention measures. Make sure all subcontractors and staff are aware of its contents.

4.   Have an emergency plan and include pollution control measures in all method statements. Make sure staff are aware of their contents.

5.   Monitor water quality before, during and after works.

6.   Monitor the flow and watercourse depth during wet and dry conditions before work begins. Size any pumps adequately to carry flow in wet conditions or during high tide.

7.   Set up designated area(s) for fuel storage and refuelling at least 10 m from the watercourse. Keep a stock of oil-absorbent materials nearby.

8.   Install straw bales or silt mats downstream of the works (Figure 9.1 and 9.2).

9.   Fix an oil-absorbent boom across the watercourse downstream of the works (Figure 9.3).

10.   Site pumps and static plant in drip trays as far away from the watercourse as possible.

11.   Where overpumping or dewatering, place the outfall pipe well downstream of the works and protect the bed and/or banks from scouring.

12.   At the end of the shift ensure pumps have sufficient fuel to run overnight if necessary.

13.   If water has collected in the working area at the start of the shift, avoid entering or disturbing the area before it can be pumped out, to minimise silt.

Figure 9.1   *Correct installation of oil-absorbent boom*

Figure 9.2   *Silt mat* (courtesy Mowlem)

Figure 9.3   *Straw bales filtering silt in newly constructed stream* (courtesy Hyder)

Access and haul routes

Avoid entry into water wherever possible. If plant or vehicles have to make repeated crossings of a watercourse, erect a temporary haul road bridge or flumed/culverted crossing (Figure 9.4).

Figure 9.4   *Haul route watercourse crossing*

Trenchless construction

Drive and reception pits should be as far from the water's edge as possible – a distance of at least 5 m is required by British Waterways (British Waterways, 2005), and up to 10 m by environmental regulators, depending on the watercourse and flood hazard.

> Pipe Jacking Association (1995). *Guide to best practice for the installation of pipe jacks and microtunnels*
>
> British Waterways (2005). *Code of practice for works affecting British Waterways*, Section 6.3 and 6.4

Bentonite and grout can cause serious harm to the water environment, as they are highly alkaline. Use of these materials must be carefully controlled to avoid breakout of bentonite in the river bed or spillage and runoff from tanks and plant at the driveshaft. A detailed site investigation is essential. The more comprehensive the results from the site investigation, the more you will be able to reduce the risk of a bentonite breakout.

CIRIA C649

Open excavations and diversions

Clay dams and sand bags are most suitable for small and/or temporary works. Clay bunds can cause water pollution when they are removed. Placing straw bales downstream of the works can help filter out any silts that are generated. Larger-scale works require dedicated silt-retention measures such as those illustrated in Figure 9.5.

Stop planks and sheet piles should be installed correctly to prevent unacceptable levels of water entering the works area (which will then need to be pumped out).

When overpumping or dewatering, place the outfall pipe well downstream of the works and provide protection to avoid scouring of the bed and/or banks.

Figure 9.5   *Silt trap comprising bags of sand used during watercourse diversion* (courtesy Balfour Beatty)

Works near water

Works alongside or near to watercourses may need consent from the environmental regulator to protect flood defence and water pollution interests.

Surface runoff is the most significant risk because of the short distance from the works to the watercourse (see Chapter 7). When removing vegetation, leave a buffer strip along the edge of the watercourse and/or around the works to filter silty runoff. You may also be able to direct runoff away to a settlement area or over grassland using earth bunds or a cut-off trench near the watercourse.

Although some bank works require "hard" bank protection, you should employ "soft" techniques wherever possible as they allow vegetation to establish at the water's edge. A simple and cost-effective method is to leave the banks and ground surface broken up (not smooth), which will allow them to revegetate naturally. Banks can be stabilised rapidly by placing upon them seeded biodegradable matting (hessian, coir etc), fibre rolls or brushwood rolls. Timber washboards, gabions, stone-filled mattresses, pitch and dry stone walls are also appropriate.

Construction alongside a sensitive watercourse

Construction involved pipeline installation alongside a stone-walled watercourse that fed a potable water supply reservoir. The topsoil was peat with clay underneath. The landscape was characterised by steep slopes and the rainfall was high.

The solution involved minimising the working width drastically, using excavated soil as a barrier to prevent runoff into the watercourse, minimising the time that the subsoil was exposed by laying short lengths of pipe, fluming the watercourse in some locations to isolate it from the works and deploying a permanent oil-absorbent boom downstream of the operation.

These measures were successful in preventing both silt and oil pollution of the watercourse and reservoir.

Works over water

When constructing bridges or similar structures, take care when slewing concrete skips or mobile concrete pump booms over open water. Follow the guidance in the environmental regulators' PPG5 Works in, near or liable to affect water.

Cleaning and painting processes over or adjacent to water have the potential to pollute. It is preferable to employ physical cleaning methods (eg wire-brushing, sand- or grit-blasting) rather than using liquid chemicals. If you do use liquids then the effluent must be fully contained (ie by the use of a bund or tray).

Carry out surface preparation and shot-blasting in a controlled manner – using sheeted enclosures will prevent dust and coarser materials from falling into the water and will allow the material to be collected and disposed of.

> Dewatering includes both lowering the water table and removing water from within excavations. Discuss your operations with the environmental regulator at an early stage so that you can obtain a licence (which can take up to four months).

Dewatering groundwater

Any groundwater abstracted will need to be discharged, ideally back to groundwater. Alternatively, it can be discharged to a watercourse or surface water drain, or (least preferable for clean water) it can be disposed of to a foul sewer. Discharged water from a well-point system is generally clean. Where silt and other potential contamination is likely, route water via a settlement tank or other treatment before discharging it under the relevant consent from the environmental regulator. Before starting work, investigate the level of risk of mobilising ground contamination into the site area.

Groundwater dewatering

1   Do not dewater without first consulting the environmental regulator.

2   Adhere to any conditions the environmental regulator has set on the volume and rate of dewatering.

3   Identify the disposal route for water and seek agreement from the environmental regulator.

4   Ensure water is treated, if necessary, to a suitable quality before it is discharged.

5   Monitor any impacts such as lowering surface water levels in nearby rivers, ponds or streams etc.

Dewatering excavations

Minimising water ingress

Successful dewatering is dependent not only on getting rid of existing water but also stopping any more getting in. Use techniques such as sheet piles, bored piles or grouting to keep out groundwater.

Surface water should not run into excavations. Divert water by digging cut-off ditches or placing sand bags or a small earth bund around the edge of the excavation. If there is water in an excavation do not allow plant or workforce to move about in it and stir up mud and silt. Fine particles such as silt and clay take a long time to settle out.

Pumping

Consider setting up a "permit to pump" procedure that requires staff to seek site management permission before pumping water (Figure 10.1). This makes sure that the appropriate regulatory permissions are in place, that the water is discharged correctly and the water quality complies with any conditions.

Set up perimeter drains and sump pumping surrounded by granular fill to avoid generating sediment – place the pump in a perforated oil drum, a short length of wide-bore pipe or concrete manhole rings and surround with granular fill in the sump.

Figure 10.1   *Permit to pump* (courtesy Alfred McAlpine)

Dewatering excavations

1   Minimise water ingress into excavations.

2   Identify disposal route for dewatered water and seek agreement from the environmental regulator/sewerage undertaker early on.

3   Use a "permit to pump" system.

4   Locate the pump in a sump to avoid generating sediment.

5   Where the water is silty or otherwise polluted, route it via a settlement tank or pond prior to discharge.

6   Install a pump of adequate size – remember that water volumes can increase significantly in wet weather.

7   Check pumps, couplings and hoses for leaks and fix as soon as possible.

8   Locate pumps on drip trays and provide simple noise screening if they are operating 24 hours a day.

Concrete, bentonite, grout and other cement-based products are highly alkaline and corrosive and can have a disastrous effect on water quality. Fish can be physically damaged (skin burns) and their gills blocked, and both vegetation and the bed of watercourses can be smothered.

It is an offence to discharge any polluting material, including cement-based products or water polluted with concrete, grout etc, into these waters without prior consent.

Concrete pollution costs contractor £4500 (The ENDS Report, Apr 2004)

A company that claims to be "one of the foremost contractors" in the UK's pipeline and utility construction sectors, was fined £4500 after killing about 100 trout in the River Calder, Lancashire.

Investigating officers found dead and dying brown trout in the river. The fish had lost their mucus covering and had burns to the eyes and fins. The company was carrying out construction work on a pipeline passing beneath the river. The contractor had obtained a land drainage consent from the Environment Agency and been advised on the need to prevent pollution. It agreed that water coming into contact with the wet concrete casing of the pipe should not be discharged to the river but should be allowed to settle before being filtered through the ground. However, the pump had been turned off for several days and water that had become extremely alkaline through contact with the cement was discharged to the river.

Alternative methods

Investigate alternative construction methods such as pre-cast or permanent formwork. Use ready-mix suppliers in preference to on-site batching in sensitive environments.

When working below the water table or in water, use hydrophilic (water-repelling) grout and quick-setting mixes or rapid hardener additives, if appropriate, to promote the early set of the surfaces exposed to water. Alternative materials, such as biodegradable shutter oils, should also be considered, particularly when working in or near water cannot be avoided.

11 Concrete and grouting activities

On-site batching

1 Locate batching and mixing activities and material storage areas well away from watercourses and drains.

2 Control surface drainage in the area around the batching plant, as it may be polluted.

3 Do not hose down spills of concrete, cement, grout or similar materials into surface water drains.

4 Washout from mixing plant or concrete lorries should be carried out in a designated, contained, impermeable area.

5 Recirculate water in batching plant where chemically suitable.

Transport and placement

It is essential to plan and supervise all activities and to adopt special procedures, particularly where there may be a risk of pollution to surface water or groundwater.

1 When working below ground, identify potential pathways for concrete or grout loss such as geological fissures.

2 Discuss arrangements for deliveries to site with suppliers prior to works – agree routes, designated washout areas and emergency procedures, particularly where there are multiple remote locations.

3 Develop procedures and a contingency plan for monitoring the use of cement-based products and uncontrolled releases.

4 Train all site personnel on method of work and emergency procedures.

5 Establish designated, clearly signed washout areas (see below).

Washout areas

Provide a designated contained washout area (or several). Where concrete is delivered to site, only wash the chutes prior to leaving site; wagons should wash out fully back at the batching plant, where facilities will be provided (see Chapter 5). For a one-off concrete pour, use a skip or lined pit. For longer-term concrete operations, or for an on-site batching plant, a series of lined ponds would be suitable.

Washout areas should be located away from watercourses, drains and protected groundwater zones and be impermeable to prevent groundwater becoming polluted. Put up clear signs and inform delivery drivers of their location (and operation if necessary).

Recirculate as much water as possible in washing activities to minimise the volume requiring disposal. Use a triggered hose and instruct operatives to use the minimum volume of water necessary. Due to the high pH (alkalinity), washout water may not be suitable for discharge to surface water drains and may even need treatment before disposal to foul sewer. In all cases a consent will be required. Hardened concrete will need to be broken out and could potentially be reused as aggregate on site. Liquid silts will need to be pumped out by a specialist contractor and disposed of in accordance with waste legislation.

Concrete, bentonite and grout

1   Check formwork and shuttering before pouring to ensure it is stable and joints are sealed to prevent loss.

2   Monitor and record the use of cement-based products during each operation.

3   Prevent concrete skips, concrete pumps and machine buckets from slewing over water where possible while placing concrete.

4   Secure the end of pump hoses by means of a rope during concreting over and adjacent to waters to prevent the discharge hose accidentally depositing concrete away from the pour site.

5   Care should be exercised when slewing concrete skips or mobile concrete pump booms over open water.

6   When placing concrete by skip, securely fasten the opening gates of the delivery chute by lock chain to prevent accidental opening over water.

7   Construct earth or sand bag barriers around bentonite and grout mixing areas, supply lines and around working areas and stockpiles of slurry arisings to prevent escape.

8   Position supply lines as far away from controlled waters and drains as possible.

9   Cover freshly placed concrete to avoid the surface washing away in heavy rain.

10 Clean up any spillages of cementitous materials immediately and dispose of correctly.

Key guidance

CIRIA R132 *A guide for safe working on contaminated sites*

CIRIA R186 *Hydraulic measures for the control and treatment of groundwater pollution*

CIRIA SP164 *Remedial treatment for contaminated land. Vol VI Containment and hydraulic measures*

CIRIA C515 *Groundwater control – design and practice*

EA, 2001. *Piling into contaminated sites*

Common examples of construction activities that present a high risk of generating pollution pathways on or adjacent to contaminated land are outlined below.

Construction activity	Pollution risks
Excavations and earthworks on contaminated land	Handling contaminated materials; generating contaminated runoff; creating vertical and horizontal pollution migration pathways
Stockpiling of contaminated soils and material	Generating contaminated runoff, discharge and dust
Tunnelling and excavations in contaminated land	Creating horizontal pollution migration pathways
Piling into contaminated land	Creating vertical pollution migration pathways
Dewatering on or adjacent to contaminated land	Drawing contaminated groundwater into on-site works; generating a contaminated discharge
Discharges to ground on contaminated land	Remobilising contamination within the unsaturated zone causing groundwater pollution
Aquifer recharge on or adjacent to contaminated land	Raising the water table and remobilising contamination within the unsaturated zone causing groundwater pollution

Site operatives should be:

- made aware of the risk of encountering unexpected contamination
- trained to recognise potentially contaminated materials
- trained to implement contingency plans and procedures.

Avoiding pollution from contaminated material

1 Do not start any construction works on or near contaminated land until a comprehensive investigation, risk assessment and specific mitigation measures have been prepared by a competent professional.

2 Always minimise the volume of contaminated material generated – eg during excavations, dewatering activities or runoff generation.

3 Divert uncontaminated runoff and surface water away from contaminated areas.

4 Do not allow site drainage to mix with contaminated discharges or liquids.

5 Control and collect all contaminated liquids and discharges, eg contaminated groundwater from dewatering activities, contaminated runoff.

6 Store all contaminated liquids in secure and bunded tanks, on an impermeable surface, for appropriate on-site treatment and/or off-site disposal at a licensed facility.

7 Do not stockpile contaminated soils and materials unless absolutely necessary.

8 If stockpiling is necessary, separate contaminated soils and materials from uncontaminated materials and store the contaminated materials on impermeable or hardstanding areas, away from watercourses and uncontaminated land.

9 Cover contaminated soils and materials to reduce the generation of contaminated dust, discharge and runoff.

10 Control and collect all runoff from the storage area for appropriate on-site treatment and/or off-site disposal.

Example contingency procedures to manage the discovery of unexpected contamination

1   Stop work immediately.

2   Inform the site supervisor and site manager.

3   Ensure all site operatives are safe.

4   Isolate and contain the area and any excavated material to reduce the risk of generating contaminated runoff, discharge or dust.

5   Inform the environmental regulator.

6   Arrange for a technical specialist to conduct chemical testing and a risk assessment.

7   Revise and develop method statements and remedial strategies accordingly.

Legislation provides protection to several hundred plant and animal species, their habitats and all bird species. Certain key species ("protected species") and certain areas ("designated sites") are protected by further legislation.

Site staff are not expected to be ecological experts, but they are expected to be reasonably aware of potential problems and to seek advice if necessary. Those who damage or disturb protected species may be prosecuted. Before mobilising to site studies should have been carried out to identify any designated ecological sites or protected species. In many instances, however, you will need to consult an environmental expert or a nature conservation body for specialist advice.

> **Key guidance**
>
> CIRIA C587 *Working with wildlife. A resource and training pack for the construction industry*
>
> CIRIA C613 *Working with wildlife pocket book*
>
> CIRIA C650 *Environmental good practice on site* (second edition)

Before working on a designated site in the UK or on one containing protected species (eg newts, certain fish, certain plants), obtain written agreement from the nature conservation body (see below). This can take several months and working methods will need to be agreed. It is an offence to start work without this permission.

The term *nature conservation* bodies is used here to represent the following organisations that have regional responsibility for ecology:

- Countryside Council for Wales

- Natural England (formerly English Nature)

- Northern Ireland Environment and Heritage Service

- Scottish Natural Heritage.

What to do when protected species are discovered on site after works have already begun

You should stop work immediately and inform the site manager, who should then seek advice from the nature conservation bodies on how to proceed.

Vegetation clearance and reinstatement

Consult with the environmental regulator and get permission before using herbicides in or near controlled waters. Only herbicides from an approved list are acceptable and their use must be in accordance with the manufacturer's product label. Staff applying herbicides in or near water require a certificate of competence.

Take particular care if reseeding or planting in conjunction with application of fertilisers that could enter and pollute watercourses through runoff.

CIRIA guidance

(Available from <www.ciriabooks.com>)

C515   *Groundwater control – design and practice* (Preene *et al*, 2000)

C587   *Working with wildlife. A resource and training pack for the construction industry* (Newton *et al*, 2004)

C613   *Working with wildlife pocket book* (Newton *et al*, 2004)

C648   *Control of water pollution from linear construction projects. Technical guidance* (Murnane *et al*, 2006)

C650   *Environmental good practice on site* (second edition) (Chant-Hall *et al*, 2005)

R132   *A guide for safe working on contaminated sites* (Steeds *et al*, 1996)

R186   *Hydraulic measures for the control and treatment of groundwater pollution* (Holden *et al*, 1998)

SP151 *Site safety handbook* (third edition) (Bielby and Read, 2001)

SP164 *Remedial treatment for contaminated land: VI containment and hydraulic measures* (CIRIA, 2005)

Pollution Prevention Guidelines

(Available from the environmental agencies)

PPG2   *Above ground oil storage tanks*

PPG4   *Disposal of sewage where no mains drainage is available*

PPG5   *Works in, near or liable to affect watercourses*

PPG8   *Safe storage and disposal of used oils*

PPG26 *Storage and handling of drums and intermediate bulk containers*

Other guidance

British Waterways (2005). *Code of practice for works affecting British Waterways.* BW, Watford

Department of Trade and Industry (2004). *Site waste management plans. Guidance for construction contractors and clients. Voluntary code of practice.* DTI, London

Environment Agency (2001). *Piling into contaminated sites*. EA, Bristol

Pipe Jacking Association (1995). *Guide to best practice for the installation of pipe jacks and microtunnels*. PJA, London

Websites

British Geological Survey <www.bgs.ac.uk>

CIRIA <www.ciria.org>

Concrete Pipeline Systems Association (CPA) <www.concretepipes.co.uk>

DTI <www.dti.gov.uk>

EHS <www.ehsni.gov.uk/>

Environment Agency <www.environment-agency.gov.uk/>

Floodline <www.environmentagency.gov.uk/floodline>

Highways Agency Research Compendium <www.ha-research.co.uk>

International Erosion Control Association <www.ieca.org>

Met Office <www.met-office.gov.uk/>

National Water Archive <www.nerc-wallingford.ac.uk/ih/nrfa/index.htm>

Netregs environmental legislation <www.environment-agency.gov.uk/netregs/>

Pipe Jacking Association <www.pipejacking.org>

SEPA <www.sepa.org.uk/

UK Society for Trenchless Technology (UKSTT) <www.ukstt.org.uk>